The Natural History Story of
White Sands
National Monument

by

Natt N. Dodge

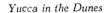

Yucca in the Dunes

Published in cooperation with
The National Park Service by
Southwest Parks and Monuments Association, Inc.
(Formerly Southwestern Monuments Association)

Southwest Parks and Monuments Association
Globe, Arizona 1971

Library of Congress Catalog Card Number: 70-78511

First Printing, 1971 — 10,000

Natural History Series No. 2

SOUTHWEST PARKS AND MONUMENTS ASSOCIATION
Globe, Arizona 85501

Printed in the United States of America

Acknowledgement

The manuscript of this book was written by former Regional Naturalist Natt N. Dodge, Southwest Regional Office, National Park Service, Santa Fe, New Mexico. It was prepared specifically to be one of the numbered Natural History Handbooks.

Restricted funds for printing delayed publication of the White Sands "story." Now, several years later, the text is being published by Southwest Parks and Monuments Association with permission of, and at the request of, the National Park Service. During the interim, the manuscript has been revised and up-dated, and has benefitted from the additional thinking of Dr. Edwin D. McKee, geologist with the U. S. Geological Survey; Mr. John R. Douglass, former Park Naturalist, White Sands National Monument; and the late H. V. Reeves.

The lavish photographic illustrations are all pictures belonging to the National Park Service.

Contents

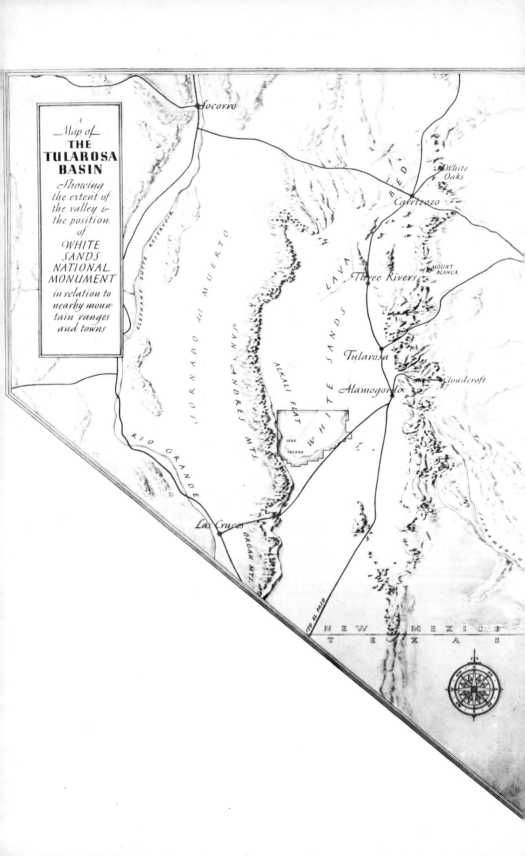

A
Map of
**THE
TULAROSA
BASIN**
Showing
the extent of
the valley &
the position
of
WHITE
SANDS
NATIONAL
MONUMENT
in relation to
nearby moun-
tain ranges
and towns

Gypsum Dunes in the White Sands

The Natural History Story of
White Sands
National Monument

THE DESERT SCENE

*W*eird, fantastic, beautiful, the largest and most impressive of the world's rare gypsum deserts lies in a flat-floored valley between the rugged parallel ranges of the San Andres and Sacramento Mountains of south-central New Mexico. Occupying the center of the long gently sloping Tularosa Basin, the immense sandscape of shimmering snow-white duneland is a trackless, timeless wilderness of sugarlike gypsum sand, vast, silent, serene.

An outstanding example of geology in action, this nearly 300-square-mile ecological island is also the home of some 60 species of hardy plants able to endure the rigors of their peculiarly restricted environment. Its scarce but intriguing animal life includes a few vigorous but strangely pale creatures that have evolved from darker colored species of the Chihuahuan Desert, which nears its northwestern limit in the brush-covered plains of the Tularosa Basin around the White Sands.

1

Footprints in the Sands of Time

WHITE SANDS: THE PLACE AND THE SANDS

*T*he Tularosa Basin, considerably larger than Delaware, Rhode Island, and the District of Columbia combined, is what geologists call a "bolson," a mountain-rimmed valley with no drainage outlet. Scientists have found evidence to indicate that thousands of years ago the basin contained a large lake,

Chihuahuan Desert and the White Sands

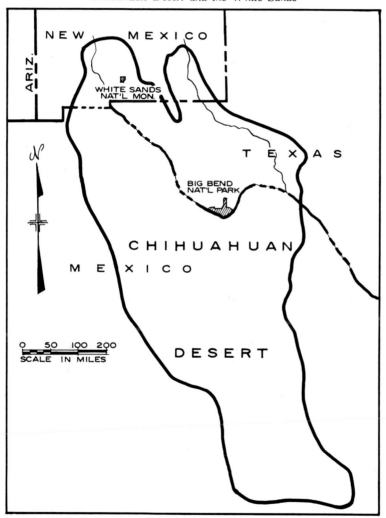

which they have named Lake Otero. Climatic changes with decreasing rainfall and increasing aridity caused the lake gradually to dry up, leaving a great playa, or alkali flat, covering 165 square miles at the nearly level, lower, western section of the valley. Part of this playa may be periodically flooded during wet weather, forming a series of wet-season lakes. The largest of these, Lake Lucero, lies within the national monument at approximately 3,880 feet above sea level, one of the lowest spots in the valley floor. Beneath the entire playa, ground water is rarely more than 3 or 4 feet, in some places only a few inches, below the surface, so the capillary action keeps the soil surface damp nearly all the time. Evaporation leaves the surface crusted with alkali, a mass of small crystals of gypsum and various sodium salts.

The mineral gypsum is hydrous sulfate of lime, or calcium sulfate combined with water ($CaSO_4 \cdot 2H_2O$). In its crystalline form it is known as selenite, and where it occurs in fine-grained massive white or delicately shaded deposits it is called alabaster. In all its forms, gypsum is soft, being given the grade of 2 in the Mohs' scale of hardness, with talc as 1 and diamond, the hardest known natural substance, as 10.

Gypsum is found in nature throughout most of the world and in commercial quantity and quality at many places in the United States. When heated to drive off part of its water, gypsum becomes plaster of paris. It is widely used in the manufacture of special types of slow-setting Portland cement, in plaster board, and in other building materials. It is also used to some extent in agriculture for treatment of soils. Chemically, gypsum is closely related to magnesium sulfate, popularly known as Epsom salt, although gypsum has little or none of the laxative effects associated with the magnesium compound. Water that is saturated with gypsum is not recommended for human consumption. In addition, such water has a corrosive action on iron: hence, iron pipes carrying solutions of gypsum or iron pipes buried in gypsum soil are short lived.

Gypsum is the earth's most common sulfate, often found in extensive beds in connection with sedimentary rocks, particularly limestone. It occurs in deposits of all ages but is especially prevalent in rocks of Silurian, Permian, and Triassic age. It has been deposited on a large scale from sea water and in smaller amounts from the waters of saline lakes. Gypsum is sometimes a product of volcanic activity and is frequently

4

found among materials deposited from the waters of hot springs. It is also associated with sulfur deposits and occurs in mineral veins where sulfuric acid has acted upon limestone.

ANCIENT SEAS: ULTIMATE SOURCE OF GYPSUM

*T*he story of the origin of the gypsum of the white sands is hidden in the rock strata of the mountains that surround the Tularosa Basin. Geologists have studied these rocks but are still trying to unravel the details of the story.

In the Permian period, some 230-280 million years ago, a large area of present-day northwestern Texas and southeastern New Mexico was submerged beneath an arm of the sea in what is called the Delaware Basin. On the northwestern side of that gulf there were bodies of water—lakes, lagoons, and bays—that were partly or at times completely cut off from the sea. Here evaporation proceeded to the point that gypsum separated from the salty ocean water. Periodically the water lost by evaporation was replaced from the ocean. Apparently part of the heavier, saltier water of the lagoons flowed out to the open sea at that time. The processes of evaporation, deposition of gypsum, and replacement of briny water continued for hundreds of centuries.

Later, as the region gradually settled lower and lower, conditions changed and other types of sediments accumulated in thick deposits on the floor of the basin. Gradually they hardened, becoming shale and limestone. Today, these rocks, and

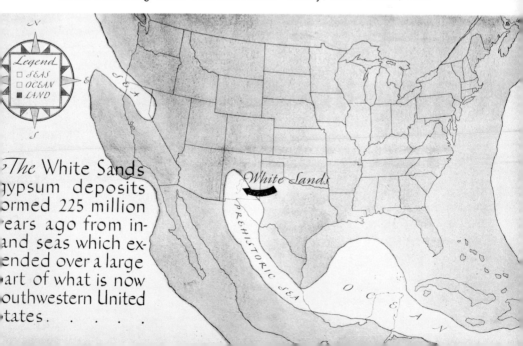

Legend
□ SEAS
□ OCEAN
■ LAND

The White Sands gypsum deposits formed 225 million years ago from inland seas which extended over a large part of what is now southwestern United States. . . . .

the gypsum-bearing Yeso Formation beneath them, are exposed on the flanks of the Sacramento Mountains, the San Andres Mountains, and the Chupadera Mesa. Especially interesting is the upper part of the Yeso Formation, in which limestone, gypsum, and shale are interbedded. The name of the formation is well chosen for a gypsum rock layer that becomes 650 feet thick in places, because Yeso is the Spanish word for gypsum or plaster. The Yeso Formation and the San Andres Limestone that lies above it have sometimes been considered as members of the Chupadera Formation.

Following the long Permian period of submersion and deposition, the land in this region gradually rose above the sea, but it was again submerged during Cretaceous times, some 90 million years in the past. About 70 million years ago a gradual uplift of the entire region set in. This long-continuing mountain-making movement, known as the Laramide revolution, or deformation, produced the Rocky Mountain chain and raised the general level of much of the land throughout the Southwest. The area which is now south-central New Mexico became a high, somewhat arched, plateauland containing the deeply buried layers of gypsum-rich rock originally formed as deposits on the floor of the ancient Permian sea.

After a long period of time, perhaps as much as 40 million years, during which continuing erosion slowly lowered the region by scouring away much of the surface formations, renewed earth movements and subsequent erosion produced the outlines of the present topography. As the result of severe faulting, which probably occurred about 10 million years ago, or as an additional movement along former crustal breaks, a massive section of the arched plateauland 100 miles long and 30 miles wide gradually settled, leaving jagged walls on either side—the scarred faces of the present Sacramento and San Andres Mountains. Because it was caused by the collapse of a fault-bordered mass of the earth's crust, the sunken area, here the Tularosa Basin, is called by geologists a graben. Since the graben is a valley with no drainage outlet, being completely surrounded by higher land, it is known further as a bolson.

During the estimated 10 million years since a section of the plateau collapsed to form the great abyss, many changes have taken place. Erosion has been at work tearing down, wearing away, and cutting back the exposed faces of the Sacramento and San Andres Mountains and carrying the debris out into

6

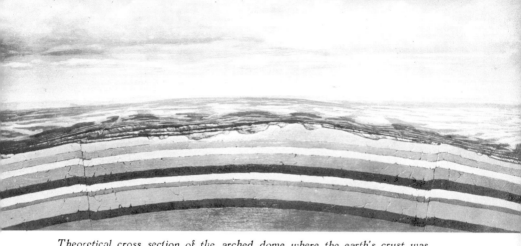

Theoretical cross section of the arched dome where the earth's crust was lifted.

Cross section of Tularosa Basin and mountain ranges to east and west, illustrating the "graben."

the valley lying between them. At the same time it cut into the higher parts of the land in the center of the graben floor. Today, only small remnants of the ridge top remain above the nearly flat floor of the basin—Two Buttes and Tularosa Peak. In them, geologists have found the same rock formations in the same relationships that occur in the mountains. For example, the cap rock of Two Buttes is San Andres Limestone, below which is the Yeso Formation. Here is support for the theory of the formation of the graben that is presented above.

Immense quantities of rock debris, including material from the gypsum-bearing Yeso Formation, have been washed into the valley from highlands at its northern end. These materials have been accumulating steadily throughout the centuries in a massive mixture and have covered the area at the base of the mountains to depths as great as 2,000 feet, building the present broad, flat valley floor that slopes gently southwestward.

GROUND WATER: PRESENT SOURCE OF GYPSUM

*A*t various times during wet periods, small lakes formed in the basin, and there is considerable evidence that Lake Otero at one time covered a large part of the valley floor. Gypsum was deposited as sediments on the floor of the lake, and evaporation left deposits of gypsum on and near the ground surface. This mineral had been dissolved in waters passing through solution channels in the Yeso Formation in the highlands around the north end of the basin and had been carried by freshets into the basin.

Since there has long been no drainage outlet, the water that entered the basin and was not lost by evaporation remained as ground water, percolating through the hundreds of feet of valley fill including many cubic miles of broken rock, much of it containing gypsum. Hence the ground water in the Tularosa Basin is thoroughly saturated with gypsum in solution.

For centuries, throughout much of the basin, the ground-water level has been only a few feet beneath the land surface, and at the lower parts of the valley floor it stood on the surface as Lake Otero. Fluctuating in size and extent as wet-weather streams poured more water into the Tularosa Basin, or as extended periods of drought reduced it by evaporation, Lake Otero long served as a huge natural evaporation pan heated by the sun.

HOW NATURE LIBERATES GYPSUM FROM WATER

*N*early everyone has watched crystals grow in a solution— perhaps when salty water evaporated on a home ice-cream machine or when making rock candy. Similarly, as ground water creeps upwards between sand grains to the surface, in the floor of dry Lake Lucero and in the Alkali Flat, the water evaporates and crystals form. At White Sands, gypsum crystallizes first, causing the grains of gypsum already present to grow a little larger. At the surface when the last water evaporates, the remaining gypsum is deposited, and then the more soluble sodium chloride (table salt) and sodium sulfate. In the past, tremendous amounts of gypsum were deposited on the floor of Lake Otero by a similar process. Imagine gypsum-bearing waters filling the lake. As evaporation went on, the water gradually became saturated with gypsum. Evaporation of water beyond that point caused gypsum to crystallize out of solution. Some of the gypsum undoubtedly settled out of solution as small sand-sized particles. Some would also have come out of solution on the surface of gypsum particles that were already there. Together with a white clay, these grains of gypsum form a white bluff that is now exposed on the western side of Lake Lucero and the Alkali Flat. Grains of gypsum, released as the wind cut into the clay and gypsum layer, were driven northeastward to form the dunes. This, in fact, has been a major source of the sands.

It appears that a deep bed of clay formed on the floor of the lake early in its existence and that gypsum grains were distributed through the clay mass. As gypsum became available from saturated lake water, these crystals grew. Because there were few of the crystals for the amount of gypsum that was available, the crystals grew to large size. This is one possible

GYPSUM IS A STANDARD MINERAL *in the* SCALE *of* HARDNESS

Minerals may be classified according to their hardness into 10 groups known as the Mohs scale. Selenite, a variety of gypsum, is the standard for #2 in this series which means that it is soft enough to be scratched by all of the minerals above it in the scale. Your fingernail is just hard enough to scratch gypsum.

❾ Corundum ❿ Diamond

❼ Quartz ❽ Topaz

❺ Apatite ❻ Orthoclase

MOHS SCALE

❶ Talc ❷ Gypsum (Selenite) ❸ Calcite ❹ Fluorite

explanation for the spectacular crystals of selenite (crystalline gypsum) that are exposed on the western side of Lake Lucero, many of which are 2 feet or more in length. Occasionally, they are in rosettes or clusters of lens-shaped crystals that grew from a common center.

Selenite crystal beds along Southwest shore of Lake Lucero. San Andres Mountains behind.

In a remarkable demonstration of erosion, soft brittle crystals of selenite the size of this booklet or larger are reduced to tiny sand-sized grains within a few miles of the crystal beds. The crystals split along the cleavage plane as they are heated during the day and cooled at night. Then they are broken by wind-driven gravel. The gravel-sized pieces of selenite roll and bounce in the winds, wearing away on the corners until they become rounded spherical and rice grain-shaped sand particles.

The water table of Lake Otero remained high throughout the lower parts of the Tularosa Basin. Gypsum-saturated moisture reaching the surface by capillarity evaporated, keeping the soil for many square miles bordering the lake encrusted with alkali. This gypsum, too, was picked up by the wind which excavated pockets in the alkali flats, and was added to the ever-growing accumulation on the valley floor—a process which is still continuing.

Some geologists discount the theory that ground water is a source of gypsum for the dunes, believing that surface gypsum is the cause rather than the result of the concentration of calcium sulfate in ground water underlying the lower part of the Tularosa Basin.

Today, selenite crystal beds underlie the remnants of Lake Otero, which probably dried up completely about 7,500 to 4,000 years ago. In subsequent periods, when the climate became more humid, water again accumulated in the Tularosa Basin, forming small Lake Lucero. The great white plain of Alkali Flat, once the bed of Lake Otero, stretches away northward along the base of the San Andres Mountains.

During rainy periods both the Alkali Flat and Lake Lucero are dotted with ponds and pools of water. When a severe cloudburst strikes the San Andres, the runoff water may fill Lake Lucero. When 9 inches of rain fell in the single month of September 1941, the Alkali Flat and Lake Lucero were filled with water, giving modern man an impression of the appearance of the ancient Lake Otero. Except for such uncommon periods of abundant moisture, Lake Lucero and the Alkali Flat are dry salt-encrusted plains, the dying stages of Lake Otero. They are plains where gypsum particles are formed continually. The gypsum is carried in by runoff from the highland around the northern end of the basin, then redeposited as the water is lost through evaporation, either from the surface of ponds and pools or from the surface of the playas or alkali flats

Jumbled maze of selenite crystals, under mesquite bush.

themselves. The processes go on today just as they did in the past, and they promise to continue indefinitely. Here is a striking example of geology in action, unnoticed by most people yet persistent, continuous, irresistible, dynamic, and expressive—a fundamental process of nature.

Stockmen in the vicinity of the White Sands have experienced for many years the strange sight of water accumulations, including Lake Lucero, taking on a rosy hue that was long believed to be caused by red algae. Biologists discovered that this color resulted from the growth of billions of microscopic plants, purple sulfur bacteria, which, under suitable conditions of temperature and other factors, develop in water having a high sulfur content. Although there is no definite time for the appearance of this phenomenon, it usually takes place in autumn.

A mile or two across the Alkali Flat to the east of Lake Lucero, the small dunes are not white but a yellowish tan. Investigation reveals that they are made up, not of rounded grains of gypsum sand, but of small flat cleavage plates larger than sand grains and resulting from the breakdown of selenite crystals eroding out along the lakeshore. Farther east are other dunes, finer grained and paler yellow, but still not the dazzling white of the dunes many miles to the northeast. As the cleavage plates of selenite are rolled and bounced along by the wind, they break into smaller and smaller particles until they attain the size and rounded shape of sand grains.

HOW WIND SORTS GYPSUM GRAINS
AND PILES THEM INTO DUNES

*W*ind is a common carrier that shows no preference as to what it transports. Wherever the wind strikes small gypsum particles that are sand-sized or even in the small gravel range, it moves them along the ground in a series of hops and skips, the smaller particles moving farther each skip than the larger particles. Thus the material is sorted as to size. As each particle strikes the sand it activates one or more other particles, which in turn are caught up and put into motion by the wind. This bombardment process is called saltation, and under a steady wind it causes the entire surface of a sand area to flow or "creep." Generally the bouncing grains of sand do not rise more than 3 feet above the surface.

13

Dunes area from the air.

Very fine particles of soil or dust are lifted high into the air and may be carried by the wind for long distances above the ground, while small pieces of rock, such as pebbles, are nudged or rolled along on the surface. Thus the wind not only effectively separates dust and pebbles from the gypsum grains but keeps the gypsum particles together. So effective is this natural winnowing process that the sand of the dunes is 96 to 97 percent calcium sulfate. At the White Sands, for many hundreds of years the southwest winds have continuously

14

Wind-blown sand resembles snow drifts.

gathered and sorted the billions of tons of gypsum sand that were progressively produced in nature's evaporation pan at the southern end of the Tularosa Basin. They have piled the sand into huge white dunes, which now cover an area of the valley floor roughly 28 miles long (north-south) and from 8 to 10 miles wide northeast of Lake Lucero—a landscape unequaled anywhere else in the world.

Sand dunes are hillocks made by windborne sand in a manner similar to that in which snow forms drifts. At White Sands National Monument the remarkable resemblance of the gypsum sand dunes to huge drifts of driven snow is particularly noticeable and is often commented upon by visitors.

The start of a dune may be caused by some object, such as a large rock, a bush, or even an irregularity in the ground, which produces a calm, or "wind shadow," behind it. Moving sand falling into this spot of quiet air accumulates, thereby adding to the size of the obstruction. Once started, the pile of sand continues to grow, soon exhibiting the characteristic shape of the dune.

Dunes assume three fundamental forms: (1) the barchan, or crescent-shaped, dune; (2) the seif, or longitudinal, dune; and (3) the transverse dune. At White Sands, the dunes are mostly of the crescentic type.

Regarding the variety of dune forms at White Sands, Dr. Edwin D. McKee, of the United States Geological Survey, wrote: "Near the source at Lake Lucero solitary or dome-

15

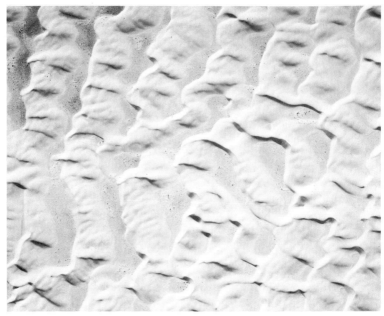

Bird's-eye view of the Gypsum dunes

Crescentic dunes in the White Sands

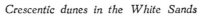

16

shaped dunes are developed; farther eastward are transverse dunes which gradually merge into barchan dunes. Near the margin of the dune area, to the east where vegetation is relatively common, the parabolic type occurs."

Because of the presence of interdunal vegetation, changes in wind direction, and other factors affecting the wind currents, there is a continual rearrangement of dune profiles so that most of them are irregular in shape and do not conform to the ideal, or simple, crescent. Also the dunes merge and run together, forming chains or colonies so that the shapes of individual dunes become lost in the maze of interlocking crests, ridges, and slopes. Thus the dunes are constantly changing, constantly shifting like the waves of a sea in slow motion. Each dune progressively migrates to leeward, owing to removal from the windward side of sand that is swept over the crest and added to the mass forming the steep fall-away face.

HOW DUNES MIGRATE

*A*lthough the dunes in White Sands National Monument vary in shape and size, they are uniform in that all their windward, or southwestern, slopes are gentle. On these slopes the angle with the horizontal varies from 3° to 10°. Winds easily drive sand grains up such inclines.

Under the pressure of a steady wind and through the process of saltation, or sand-grain impact, there is a sorting of the particles, the larger ones accumulating to form small ridges, roughly at right angles to the wind direction. These small ridges give the gentle windward slopes of the dunes a rippled appearance, which adds greatly to their esthetic appeal and their attraction for photographers.

Each dune is surmounted by a sharp crest with a steep leeward slope, or slip face, of loose sand. Even during high winds, the leeward side is in relative calm; hence, sand swept up the windward face is catapulted over the top to be dropped into the void in the lee of the crest. During steady winds a constant visible mist of sand pours over the crest of each dune, building up on the leeward slip face until the angle of repose reaches about 35°. Then a mass of loose sand avalanches down the slip face, sometimes all the way to the ground at its base. The entire face does not slump at once, but during steady winds there may be a slip every few moments so that the combined

17

Reverse winds cause spectacular blowouts.

effect is one of a gradual forward movement of the entire dune. Transfer of sand from the windward slope to the lee- ward face causes the dunes to march in the same direction as the prevailing wind unless the sand, as on marginal dunes, is held down or stabilized by a mat of vegetation.

Dunes may advance several feet or even yards during a windy period of a few days duration, but there are, of course, long periods of quiet weather during which there is little wind and no forward movement. Also, there are occasional times when "reverse" winds from the north or northeast turn the crests of the dunes back upon themselves, causing "blowouts" in the loose sand of the slip faces and forming small "negative" dunes on the tops of the large ones. Similar negative dunes are formed by persistent winds from the east and southeast during the summer. These superimposed crest dunes with their slip faces toward the south or southwest are temporary and are soon erased by the recurrence of the dominant southwesterly winds.

"How fast are the dunes moving? Preliminary measure- ments yield a picture of rapidly moving dunes on the western edge of the dune field, with a gradual decrease in movement

18

through it. At the eastern margin there is measurable advancement at a few active points, though the rate of advance along most of this margin appears to be only a few inches a year, if any. Thirty feet of movement to the northeast in 1 year by a small dune on the western margin of the dunes is the fastest rate so far recorded. In the vicinity of the picnic area small dunes show a movement of 10 to 12 feet a year. Larger dunes move more slowly than smaller ones because a greater amount of sand must be transported by the wind to achieve the same amount of dune movement.

HOW GYPSUM DUNES AFFECT LOCAL VEGETATION, AND VICE VERSA

*I*n this strange gypsum desert, living creatures have found a harsh, forbidding, and inhospitable environment. Nevertheless during past centuries species of both plants and animals have adapted to the unusual habitat and have developed ways and means to survive, reproduce, and spread under the unique conditions presented by the sea of sand. Thus the area is a strange, white ecological island where unique conditions have produced plant and animal associations quite different from those in the normal Chihuahuan Desert regions surrounding it.

The chemical and physical characteristics of the duneland present hazards to plants and animals. Foremost is the nearly continual motion of the sand, which exposes the roots of plants in one place while it buries plants in another place. Mineral nutrients are another problem, for some that are required by plants seem to be missing. Though the sands are 96 to 97 percent calcium sulfate, and ground water supplies such elements as potassium, nitrogen, iron, chlorine, boron, and silicon, no evidence of others has been reported. Surely there is a source of phosphorus that is required for plant life, but it has not been detected. Also missing are the micronutrients, often called trace elements, copper, manganese, molybdenum, and zinc, some of which most plants require for health and growth.

Scientists have discovered seams of bright-green algae, single-celled plants, just beneath the surface in interdunal depressions. Gelatinous masses of these tiny primitive plants (which also appear as black-green patches on the surface) contribute to stabilizing the surface crust. Capable of obtaining

Survival of vegetation along fronts of marginal dunes depends on ability to adjust to physical and chemical conditions imposed by the gypsum sand.

20

nitrogen from the atmosphere, they provide a continually renewable source of soil nitrogen essential to the survival and growth of vegetation.

There is no critical shortage of moisture in the white sands. Although rainfall is scant (only 6 to 10 inches a year), much of the precipitation sinks into the sand, which is usually moist a few inches beneath the dry surface. Also, the water table is only 3 or 4 feet beneath much of the surface of the dune area and the adjacent Alkali Flat. Even though it is saturated with gypsum in solution, this ground water is not difficult for many plants to assimilate, but it is unpalatable and noxious for animals.

Temperatures among the dunes vary greatly, not only seasonally but during almost any 24-hour period. Certain animals, especially reptiles, are extremely sensitive to temperature changes, and their activities are markedly influenced by them. Records made on one summer day show that the temperature on the sand surface rose from 58° F. at 5 a. m. to 118° at 1 p. m., and even greater temperature variations are known to occur. Still, the sands are cooler than the darker earth outside the dunes. Since the white surface of the sand reflects rather than absorbs both light and heat from the sun, there is a rapid drop in temperature and light intensity in the dune area following sunset even after the hottest summer day.

Scientists studying the effect of the white sands and the lava beds in the northern end of the valley upon the plants and animals of the Tularosa Basin recognize four ecological groupings, or plant associations, outside of the dune area. Three of these, the creosotebush, mesquite, and saltbush associations, occupy adjacent broad belts lying parallel to the base of the Sacramento Mountains and are found in that order as you proceed across the basin from the foot of those mountains toward the dunes of white sand. These associations reflect the gradually increasing content of alkaline salts in the soil toward the dunes. A fourth, the grassy wash association, cuts across the others, following the winding courses of ephemeral runoff streams that flow from the mountains after rainstorms.

Within the white sands themselves, scientists have named three vegetative groupings, or plant associations. First, vegetation of the yucca-sumac association is fairly heavy among the relatively stable gypsum hillocks near the outer edges of the sands, becoming rapidly less dense toward the interior of the

Note heavy growth in left background, at outer edges of sands, and fairly stable shrub growth between the marginal dunes.

In depression at right note smaller plant growth of gramagrass-joint-fir association.

duneland. Second, depressions between perimeter, or marginal, dunes are occupied by a considerable variety of smaller plants of the gramagrass-joint-fir association. Far out in the duneland, although no vegetation can gain a foothold on the continually shifting surfaces of the moving dunes, a few hardy plants, with the small animals that they shelter and support, occupy the level, constantly changing, interdunal spaces. These plants make up the third, or ricegrass-little bluestem association.

HOW SOME PLANTS SUCCESSFULLY RESIST BURIAL BY ADVANCING DUNES

*B*etween the open glistening heart of the brilliant active duneland and the vegetated stabilized gypsum hillocks along the outer fringes of the sands, there is a zone of obvious conflict. In this battleground are the weird skeletons of plants which have temporarily withstood the onslaught of the dunes, only to be finally smothered by the overwhelming masses of moving sand. Here are grotesquely bent yuccastalks covered with a snarl of adventitious roots, plants that have extended themselves to withstand burial only to be left behind naked and unprotected as the dune passed on. Here are the great white drifts surmounted by vigorous shrubs that flaunt their foliage from the very crests of dunes that have failed to submerge them. Here are bizarre pedestals of hardened gypsum, bound into columns by a matted tangle of elongated stems, bearing on their shoulders the bushy plants that conquered the dunes only to be left behind tenaciously holding such sand as their many stems could encompass as the dune moved on. Here the tide

Far out in the Duneland a few hardy plants gain a short-lived foothold on the constantly shifting interdunal flats.

Bizarre pedestals of hardened gypsum support bushy plants that conquered the dunes only to be left behind when drifts of sand moved on.

of battle swings back and forth, always shifting, never static.

A new growth of plants taking hold in the interdunal depressions forever challenges the forefront of advancing dunes. Those few victorious shrubs that successfully withstood the attack and pushed their crowns upward through the smothering gypsum to ride the crests are too scattered to more than slow down the dunes' irresistible advance.

In this intermediate belt where dune movement has been retarded but where sandhill migration still continues northeastward under the influence of the dominant winds, at least eight perennials (of the 62 species of plants which are able to grow in the high concentration of calcium sulfate in the dune field) have developed an ability to resist being overwhelmed and smothered by advancing dunes. Through growth of the stem tips, these plants when threatened with burial are able to extend themselves fast enough to keep the crowns of their elongating stems above the surface of the steep faces of the oncoming dunes. After herculean struggles with the smothering sand mass, they eventually appear triumphant on the summits of the dunes. Soaptree yucca plants with snakelike stems 30 feet long have been reported. Such extreme elongation is rare, for the dunes in this zone usually are not more than 15 or 20 feet high.

Cross section of dune showing
extended yucca stem whose roots
are in soil beneath the dune.

Cottonwood tree roots extending laterally beneath the sands are exposed by wind.

Two of the eight burial-resistant species build spectacular columns, or pedestals: the Rio Grande cottonwood, the only plant attaining tree size among the dunes; and skunkbush sumac.

As the lengthening trunk of a cottonwood pushes upward, it sends out hundreds of adventitious, or out-of-place, roots into the surrounding sand, binding the sand into a compact mass held firmly around the trunk of the growing tree. As time passes and the dune gradually moves on, it leaves the cottonwood behind, its trunk wrapped in a root-bound plaster cast. After a number of years, during which time the dune has moved on in its entirety, the tree remains standing alone in the open interdunal flat, to all appearances a large-crowned, short-trunked tree atop a column of compacted gypsum. Actually, the tree's feeding roots are widespread in the moist soil far beneath the sand, and its long trunk is hidden within the column of gypsum held tightly about it by the unseen mass of adventitious roots.

Skunkbush sumacs, atop their stem-bound gypsum columns, are much more numerous than cottonwoods, and in some places they dominate the landscape. Not as tall as cottonwoods, the sumacs are more massive and incite the curiosity of visitors who express wonder as to how these big bushes managed to grow on the compact piles of gypsum. Other prominent if less spectacular mound-forming burial-resistant plants are the Torrey ephedra, or Mexican tea, fourwing saltbush, and rubber rabbitbrush. These bushy shrubs are less hardy than the sumacs, yuccas, and cottonwoods and are usually found among the younger, smaller interdunal flats.

The two remaining burial-resistant plants are less noticeable than the pedestal and mound builders but are just as effective in anchoring the sand, thereby retarding its movement. Hoary rosemarymint produces vinelike prostrate stems that, through rapid tip growth, are able to remain above the accumulating drift and, at the dune surface, develop into normal leafy-stemmed plants about 3 feet high. Comandra, or falsetoadflax, believed to be partially parasitic on cottonwood roots, when buried in sand develops an extensive system of rhizomes, or underground stems, which send out numerous sandbinding rootlets. These stems elongate abnormally, thereby bringing the leafy part of the plant into the air and sunlight on top of the dune.

Extensive root development as well as abnormal stem elongation is characteristic of the shrubby plants that survive within the belt of inner marginal dunes. Vertical taproots extend deeply into the gypsum-impregnated soil beneath the dunes, and long slender lateral roots run beyond the limits of the individual mounds. The extent of these shallow underground root systems is sometimes spectacularly revealed by wind erosion, which in places has exposed 10- to 20-foot

27

lengths of cottonwood, skunkbush sumac, and hoary rosemary-mint roots.

During the spring and sometimes other seasons, the vegetation is subject to blasting by strong winds carrying sand. These gypsum particles injure the plants directly by abrasion, sometimes scouring away the bark from stems and exposed roots on the windward side, principally within 2 feet of the ground, because the blowing sand rarely rises higher than that above the surface. Mechanical injury is augmented by desiccation, owing to the drying effect of the arid atmosphere.

HOW ACTION OF ADVANCING GYPSUM IS SELECTIVE

*A*long the extreme eastern and northeastern borders of the sands, the gypsum dunes, restrained by the sand-binding stems and adventitious roots of the vegetation which has stubbornly resisted their movement, nevertheless advance slowly upon the adjacent desert plain. The plant population remaining within the area of encroachment consists of species capable of adjusting both to the movement of the sand and to the concentration of calcium sulfate. The many other species native

Vigorous shrubs occupy crests of dunes that have failed to submerge them.

28

Growth in depressions between peripheral dunes.

to the normal soil of the Tularosa Basin are either smothered
by burial or fail to endure the high gypsum content of the
sandcovered soil. Thus the survival of vegetation along the
forefront of peripheral dunes depends upon ability of the
various species to adjust to the abnormal chemical and physical conditions which the encroaching sand imposes upon them.

Of 228 species of plants recorded throughout the Tularosa
Basin, only 62 have been found within the area of influence of
the gypsum accumulation. The majority of these are in the
gramagrass-joint-fir association covering depressions between
the peripheral dunes and between them and the monument
boundaries.

Although abundant, the desert-type vegetation of White
Sands National Monument consists in general of drab, un-
spectacular herbs and small shrubs. Most of the flowering
plants are scattered and inconspicuous. Perhaps the most noticeable, especially when in bloom during late May and early
June, are the stiffly erect soaptree yuccas. Because of its nar-
row, slender, spine-tipped leaves, this member of the lily family
is sometimes mistaken by visitors for some sort of cactus. The
large open clusters of creamy bell-shaped blossoms, State
flower of New Mexico, are borne on tall stalks. The withered
blooms are replaced by brown capsule fruits that persist for
months and attract almost as much attention as the blossoms.

29

BLOOMING TIMES OF WHITE SANDS FLOWERING PLANTS

*W*hite Sands National Monument is not noted for massed flower displays nor for any species, except possibly the torch cactus, which is outstandingly spectacular. There are many flowering plants, however, that attract attention and arouse curiosity. The list on page 31 provides a guide to some of the more common and noticeable flowers:

LIFE IN THE OPEN SPACES BETWEEN ACTIVE DUNES

*A*lthough the ever-shifting sand surfaces of active dunes offer no opportunities for even the most hardy plants to gain a foothold, the extensive windswept, gypsum-impregnated soil flats between dunes provide a stable, if temporary, base for a few plants able to endure the sweeping wind and the high concentration of calcium sulfate.

One of these is pickleweed, also called iodinebush because of the color of the dried sap. This somewhat drab plant, 2 or 3 feet tall, with small fleshy leaves, will tolerate soils of high alkalinity even to the extent of growing sparsely on the otherwise entirely barren gypsum-encrusted flats west of the dunes. It is abundant in low areas where pools form after rains between marginal dunes, but it is lacking in the interior dune area. Its plentiful pollen causes hay fever in some persons.

Only a relatively few species of plants are adapted to survive in the constantly changing interdunal flats within the active interior of the sands. Because of the advance of the dunes, each of these depressions is also shifting as the leeward dune advances, leaving open ground in its wake on the north side of the flat. On the opposite side of the flat the windward dune's slip face marches forward, burying the south side of the interdunal space under tons of loose sand. The perennial plants that get footholds in these interdunal flats are inevitably submerged by an on-marching dune. Estimates of dune movement suggest that the plants have a chance for life between the dunes for periods ranging from a few years to about 20 years. In the region of greatest dune movement, in a band about a quarter-mile-wide on the western edge of the sands, plants are not able to survive at all.

30

Blooming time	Plant	Color	Where Found
Early spring	Gilia	White	Widespread among marginal dunes.
April-June	Mint shrub	Purple	Abundant on marginal dunes.
Spring	Buttonweed, or sida	Red-Orange	Plains around dune area.
Spring	Mustard	White	Flats between marginal dunes.
Feb. to Aug.	Spectaclepod	Yellow	Edges of marginal dunes.
March-Sept.	White Sands sandverbena	Pink	Flats throughout the dunes.
March-June	Locoweed, halfmoon loco	Purple	Flats south of dunes.
April-Sept.	Yellow-flowered evening-primrose	Yellow	Flats among marginal dunes.
May-Sept.	White-flowered evening-primrose	White	Flats throughout the dunes.
April-May	Torch cactus	Bright-red	Plains bordering dune area.
May-June	Woolly paperflower	Yellow	Among marginal dunes.
May-June	Walkingstick cholla	Deep-red	Plains bordering marginal dunes.
May-June	Pricklypear cactus	Yellow to pink	Plains bordering marginal dunes.
May-July	Soaptree yucca	Creamy white	Flats among dunes.
Summer	Blazingstar	Yellow	Flats among marginal dunes.
Late Summer	Moonpod	Greenish white	Flats among dunes.
Late Summer	Centaury	Rose-pink	Flats among dunes.
Late Summer	Snakeweed	Yellow	Flats among marginal dunes.
Late Summer	Rubber rabbitbrush	Yellow	Plains around marginal dunes.

Note: Observed as late as October: White Sands sandverbena, pepperweed, rubber rabbitbrush, groundsel, aster, goldenweed, sunflowers, and woolly paperflower. Several spring bloomers flower again following the summer rains, which usually begin in July.

31

The sparse interdunal vegetation, growing as small hummocks on the gypsum-encrusted soil, is principally Indian ricegrass and little bluestem (grass). An occasional clump of alkali sacaton (grass) or a lonesome yucca or ephedra, two of the burial-resistant species, is infrequently found far out among the sea of active dunes. Here, too, is found the indigenous White Sands sandverbena, which blossoms from March to July and sometimes in September. Its pale-pink flower heads seem delightfully out of place amid the severe surroundings. Another alkali-resistant small shrub, common throughout the sands wherever vegetation is found, is frankenia. It is one of the few species occasionally found on interior dune flats and among embryonic dunes near Lake Lucero.

Nocturnal creatures leave a delicate tracery of tracks on the pristine surface of the sand.

LIFE AMONG THE DUNES

*T*his rather forbidding interdunal habitat, with little to offer animals in the way of food or shelter, supports a sparse population of small mammals, insects, and reptiles. Some of these wander up onto the pristine surfaces of the surrounding dunes where they leave a delicate tracery of tiny tracks soon erased by the fitful breezes.

Many insects are found dead on the dunes, possibly overcome by midday heat. A species of predacious white camel cricket is sometimes seen at night on windward surfaces of the dunes. Its body covering is so transparent that its internal organs are readily visible. A light-colored spadefoot toad (the Great Plains spadefoot) and a small pale scorpion (Northern scorpion) have been recorded in the sands. They are probably not numerous and are rarely seen. Light-colored tiger beetles are active at night. This departure from normal day-hunting of tiger beetles elsewhere indicates an escape method of adaptation to a harsh environment.

Owing to the intense light and extreme heat of midday, most creatures of the interdunal flats seek shelter in the soil or sand, coming out to forage during early morning and late afternoon hours, or they may become completely nocturnal. Night-flying predators are probably as great an enemy as their severe habitat.

Although a large animal such as a coyote, striped skunk, badger, porcupine, or kit fox is occasionally seen far out in the ocean of dunes, these are not common visitors and have very little influence on resident population of the interdunal flats. Largest and most abundant mammal inhabitant of the Indian ricegrass-little bluestem interdunal plant association is the sands pocket gopher, (a local relative of the eastern or plains pocket gopher), whose numerous burrows provide hiding places and retreats from the sun for Apache pocket mice, wolf spiders, and the little White Sands swifts. The last named are small, agile lizards that stalk and capture insects during cooler hours of early morning and late afternoon.

Predacious darkling beetles, or "stink bugs," inactive during heat of midday, are busy foragers during early morning, late afternoon, and possibly at night. These large coal-black insects are glaringly conspicious against the white background of the sand, but they are apparently immune to predation by

33

Protected from most enemies by the unpleasant odor associated with its striking black-and-white coat, the striped skunk is not feared by the great horned owl.

Darkling beetle

birds. If they taste as unpleasant as they smell when crushed, their conspicuous appearance is a warning to would-be attackers. Some species have no odor but are protected by being as black as their noxious relatives. Children are intrigued by them as they stalk stiff-legged across the sands, assuming an amusing headstand when disturbed, their posteriors pointed skyward.

In some places the flats between dunes are undermined with pocket gopher tunnels and dotted with mounds of earth pushed

A porcupine occasionally wanders into shrubs bordering the dunelands.

35

from them. Old mounds invariably have little bluestem grass growing on them. There is a possible ecological relationship between this grass and the pocket gopher. In foraging, the gophers follow wellworn trails leading from their burrow mounds into the surrounding flat, but they rarely go more than 6 feet from the entrance to their tunnels. Hawks and owls are their chief enemies, for other predators rarely invade the vast stetches of open barren duneland.

Three other rodent species—the long-tailed deer mouse, spotted ground squirrel, and Apache pocket mouse—are found sparingly throughout the entire white sands area and are more numerous in the interior of the ocean of sand than as components of the life communities of the more heavily vegetated peripheral dunes.

LIZARDS AND POCKET MICE: SURVIVAL OF THE FITTEST

*T*hree white lizards and a white mouse are outstanding examples of adaption to the white environment of the gypsum sands. Foremost among them is the bleached earless lizard *(Holbrookia maculata ruthveni)*. It can turn so completely white that it is invisible as it lies on the open sand near an ant colony, waiting for a tasty meal to come its way. Though it can change color to match the darker areas between dunes, and may become quite dark when hurt, cold or scared, the ability to become white remains the outstanding characteristic of this species. It often feeds in the open where its white camouflage and the dazzling reflection of light from its smooth tiny scales are its only protection from predators. During the mating period in early summer the females achieve a remakable pink to orange blush of color along their sides.

The other two species of lizards, the white sands swift *(Sceloporus undulatus cowlesi)* and the little striped whiptail *(Cnemidophorus inornatus)* show ability to change the tan parts of their bodies to completely white, but they normally do not rely on this for protection. They spend their lives in or near clumps of vegetation. The swift will often dash into the sheltering bush where it is well camouflaged because its light-colored striped pattern blends with the pattern of twigs and branches. The whiptail, which has a long bright-blue tail, can not rely on camouflage for protection nearly as much, though

Camouflage in the White Sands. The bleached earless lizard.

it can turn the tan parts of its body nearly white. Whenever danger threatens, it normally dashes for a hole in the sand under a bush.

It is thought that these three lizards developed through the centuries because the white environment made normally brown individuals easily visible to predators. Individuals with ability to turn the palest color would have the best chance of survival and reproduction under such conditions. As generations followed one upon the other, the palest individuals surviving the longest in each generation, the entire population came to have the white coloration it has today.

The pale Apache pocket mouse has caused something of a stir among zoologists because of its remarkable color adaptation to its environment. These blond mice are difficult to see even when moving about the sand, but when they "freeze," remaining perfectly motionless, they blend so effectively into their pallid surroundings that they are easily overlooked by such predators as owls, hawks, and foxes. Their color, or lack of it, serves to conceal and protect them.

The bleached appearance of the white sands race of pocket

37

The bleached appearance of the White Sands race of pocket mice is of special interest to zoologists.

mice is especially noteworthy because individuals of the same genus that inhabit nearby Tularosa Basin lands having reddish soils are generally rusty in appearance. Other pocket mice living within the dark volcanic rocky jumble of the lava beds north of the sands are almost black. The contrast in appearance between individuals of these three races effectively illustrates the principle of animal adaptation to factors of their environments and spotlights survival value of appropriate coloration.

Scientists point out that differentiation in color of these three races of mice resulted because only those individuals which escaped ther predatory foes lived to reproduce. Among the white sands, lighter colored individuals were more effectively concealed; hence the pale ones lived and, through many generations, developed a race of which all individuals matched the tone of their surroundings. In the lava beds the darker colored mice survived, thereby building a dark-pelaged race there; while in the red soil region, a race of rust-colored mice became prevalent.

Seeds of little bluestem grass and of the rubber rabbitbrush are relished by the pocket mice and probably constitute their principal food.

INSECTS: IMPORTANT MEMBERS OF THE WHITE SANDS LIFE COMMUNITIES

Cooperation between the yucca plants and the small yucca moths, numerous among the marginal dunes, provides a classic illustration of mutual dependence. As soon as the yucca blossoms open, the female moth, having specially modified mouth parts, enters one and scrapes together into a ball the sticky pollen from the stamens. Carrying it to another flower she mounts the pistil and, penetrating with her ovipositor the wall of the ovary, lays her eggs in the seed cavity. She then places the ball of pollen on the pistil, carefully rubbing it into the stigmatic tube and thus assuring fertilization and development of the seeds, some of which will serve as food for the larvae after the eggs hatch. Without the moth, the yucca blossoms would not be pollinated; without the developing yucca seeds, the young of the moth would have no food.

Insects are abundant in the white sands and vicinity, where extensive collections were made by Dr. Clyde P. Stroud, of the University of Chicago, during the summer of 1947. Of 371 species of insects taken, 263 were collected in and near the edge of the dune area. The number of species and of individuals diminishes rapidly from the outer parts of the dune area inward, owing to abrupt decline in vegetation upon which the insects are dependent for food and shelter. Peripheral dunes furnish suitable habitats for more species of insects than level plains of the valley floor surrounding the white sands, because of the presence on and between the frontal dunes of a greater variety of plant species than over an area of like size in other parts of the Tularosa Basin.

Most notable of these plants, from the standpoint of insects associated with it, is the soaptree yucca, on which Dr. Stroud found 67 species of insects. In addition to the yucca moth and the sulphur butterfly, aphids, long-horned beetles, and flesh flies occur in sufficient numbers to indicate possible ecological relationships with the yucca.

On various grasses, 44 species of insects have been observed. Large aggregations of flea beetles feed on the endemic yellow-flowered evening-primrose. Fourteen insect species are associated with rabbitbrush, and a similar number have been observed on Rio Grande cottonwood. Chalcid wasps were observed emerging from seed capsules of hoary rosemarymint. Cicadas are numerous in July on fourwing saltbush and skunkbush sumac. Snout weevils, lady beetles, and grasshoppers are common. One nest of harvester ants was found, some distance from any vegetation, at the base of a dune.

Although absence of adaptation to ground color is more strkiing than its presence among the insects, species which definitely do show the influence of their white environment include a camel cricket, grasshopper, tiger beetle, and possibly an ant. Some of the snout beetles are white—others, apparently the same species, are quite dark. Several insects, as well as wolf spiders and centipedes, found within the sands may be somewhat lighter in color than members of the same species occupying the valley floor beyond the margins of the dune area.

MARGINAL DUNES: HOME OF MANY SMALL ANIMALS

Although their ability to move about renders animals less restricted than plants to a specific site, they are all de-

40

pendent upon plants and animals of a particular environment for their four major requirements: food, shelter, defense from enemies, and suitable conditions for raising families. In general, individuals establish territories which they guard zealously and within which they remain except for occasional forays into their neighbors' ranges. Attachment to a familiar area satisfying all of these essentials for existence seems to be a characteristic of most small earth-bound creatures. Some individuals may live their entire lives within the same home range. When an area becomes too crowded or the food supply becomes seriously reduced, however, there are shifts to other areas.

Whereas only a few species of animals have been able to adapt their requirements to the rigid conditions which prevail among active dunes, a considerable variety of small creatures find food. shelter, protection, and nesting facilities in the relatively heavily vegetated and partly stabilized peripheral sand hills and plains surrounding them. These, with the plants and attendant insects, form an intricate and interdependent web of life—the plant-animal communities of the marginal dune environment.

A community could not long endure without a relatively stable, even though continually fluctuating, balance between plant-eaters and meat-eaters and between hosts and parasites. Such relationships maintain a balance among species and prevent certain species from becoming so abundant as to destroy their habitat and eventually themselves. Animals are adapted to the physical, biological, and climatic conditions which characterize their habitats and are extremely sensitive to any changes in them. Thus they remain within suitable environmental boundaries but have the inherent ability to modify their requirements or to spread into surrounding areas with different characteristics if necessary.

Although no complete study has been made of White Sands National Monument's animal inhabitants, certain investigations, along with numerous observations recorded by National Park Service personnel, have inventoried 144 species of birds, 23 of small mammals, 371 species of insects, and a few reptiles.

In addition to the three species of lizards mentioned previously—bleached earless lizard, White Sands swift, and little striped whiptail—several other species of lizards prey on insects in the areas outside the sands. Most commonly seen are the desert side-blotched lizard and the marbled whiptail. The latter

Western diamondback rattlesnakes occur here, but few people are lucky enough to see one.

is often seen in the brush near buildings. He causes a lot of comment because of his spectacular long blue tail.

Snakes are rarely seen among the gypsum dunes, where they would have neither shelter nor dependable food supply. Several species, however, inhabit parts of the monument where vegetation provides the shade which all reptiles require in hot

Gopher snakes prefer the brushy habitat outside of the duneland.

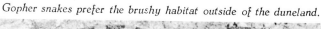

weather, because their bodies contain no temperature-regulating mechanism. Although western diamondback rattlesnakes and prairie rattlesnakes are present, they are not numerous and are rarely seen. In common with the gopher snake and the long-nosed snake, they inhabit vegetated flats outside of the dune aea where small rodents, their principal food, are fairly abundant. Like the lizards, they remain quiet in the shade during the heat of a summer's day, going abroad to hunt after dark or when the sun is low. Checkered garter snakes are occasionally seen in the swampy area bordering Garton Pond in an eastern extension of the monument. These semiaquatic reptiles are active during the daytime, feeding on insects, amphibians, and small fish.

In common with snakes which, in general, subsist on rodents, insects, young birds, and other small creatures, the larger mammals of White Sands are principally predators. Occasionally reported far out among the active dunes where they are visible for miles, both coyotes and kit foxes, although by no means common, are more numerous in the brushy cover of the marginal dunes and vicinity where rodents are abundant and where they can remain well hidden. Both hunt at night; however, coyotes are sometimes active during daylight hours. Tracks of both are often seen in the loose gypsum of frontal dunes.

Another predator which is rarely seen, but whose unmistakably large burrows afford mute testimony of its presence, is the badger. This short-legged member of the weasel family and relative of the skunk is equipped with powerful front legs, armed with long, strong claws. They enable it to dig rapidly, either to capture a rodent in its burrow or to escape from an enemy. Coyotes have been known to attack badgers, whose heavy muscular bodies, strong forelegs, and belligerent dispositions make them formidable antagonists.

Among the larger vegetarians inhabiting the fringe dunes and adjoining parts of the monument are the desert cottontail and black-tail jackrabbit. Both are common throughout the Tularosa Basin. The few porcupines which have been seen in the area were first thought to be strays that had wandered into the Tularosa Basin from the mountains to the east or west, but recent reports indicate that they are seen in the monument the year round, and are now believed to be resident.

Three species of kangaroo rats have been observed in the

The black-tailed jackrabbit is one of the larger vegetarians.

Kangaroo rats are rarely seen by day

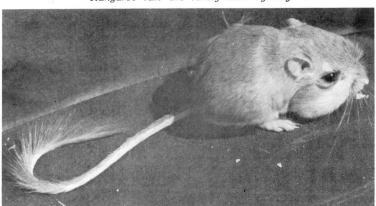

yucca-sumac association among the marginal dunes, but are not as abundant in the monument as in other parts of the Tularosa Basin. These burrowing rodents have fur-lined cheek pouches in which they cram seeds for transport to their burows, using their forepaws as nimble hands. They also eat some vegetation and an occasional insect. Their oversize hindlegs enable them to hop along in an upright position, using the long brush-tipped tail as a balancing organ. Kangaroo rats are nocturnal and are practically never seen in the daytime, remaining

44

in their extensive underground tunnels, along which food caches are located at intervals.

The kangaroo rat is host, willingly or not, to numbers of neighbors that make use of his underground passages for shelter and to escape the heat of the day. Among these are lizards, gopher snakes, spiders, centipedes, and a variety of insects. Abandoned kangaroo rat burrows are sometimes taken over by pocket mice or gasshopper mice, both of which are found among the marginal dunes.

As its name implies, the grasshopper mouse feeds chiefly on insects, but it is a ferocious hunter and preys on pocket mice, harvest mice, small kangaroo rats, an occasional lizard, and even other grasshopper mice. Only about one-tenth of its food is vegetation, mostly grass seeds. Since it does not hibernate but remains active all winter, it must rely to some extent on vegetable food when insects are absent or dormant.

The western harvest mouse is another shy and retiring inhabitant of the marginal dunes environment. It is rarely seen by monument visitors but its nests are occasionally found and record its presence. The nest, about the size and shape of a baseball, is made of grasses firmly woven among the branches of a low shrub. There is only one entrance, about a half-inch in diameter, penetrating the woven sphere. Usually two broods of young, in litters of two to four, are raised annually. Harvest mice are active principally at night, gathering seeds which they usually eat on the spot. Although they sometimes carry food back to the nest, they have no storehouses.

Famous in legend and story of the West, the woodrat, or packrat, adds interest to the rodent population of the marginal dunes area. Scarce in numbers and nocturnal in its way of life, it is rarely seen. However, specimens which have been studied show marked characteristics, such as lighter colored pelage, that differ from those of its close relative, the southern plains woodrat, indicating that a race of pale individuals may be developing among the dunes. The woodrat is noted for its custom of carrying to its nest objects which attract its fancy. Its habit of dropping one object to pick up another of greater appeal has given it the name of trade rat.

Famous in western legend and story, the woodrat is a very interesting rodent at White Sands. (See next page)

Torrey ephedra with stiff, leafless stems and tiny yellow flowers, locally called Mexican tea.

PLANTS: COLOR IN THE SANDS

*H*ost to 43 species of insects, fourwing saltbush (often mis-called "sagebrush" by persons unfamiliar with Chihuahuan Desert vegetation) is a shrub with small gray-green leaves and tiny light-yellow flowers. Its large clusters of papery pale-green four-vaned fruits attract attention and arouse curiosity. The leaves have a salty taste—hence the name.

Another common shrub is the Torrey ephedra, or joint-fir,

47

Yellow flowered evening-primrose

whose apparently leafless green to yellow-green stiff stems give it prominence. In spring its clusters of small yellow blossoms attract many insects. From the dried stems pioneers brewed a palatable tonic beverage, giving the plant the local names Mexican tea and Mormon tea. The fruits resemble tiny cones.

Of the few plants whose blossoms attract attention, the small yellow-flowered evening-primrose is of particular interest because the variety is indigenous to the white sands and is not

Buffalo gourd, or coyote melon.

found elsewhere. The plant is fairly common among the marginal dunes and is noticeable, when in blossom, along the road leading into the heart of the duneland. This species blooms profusely in May and again following the first rains of summer, which usually begin in July.

Hikers among the peripheral dunes sometimes come across a plant whose long spreading vinelike stems, large triangular leaves, and attractive orange-yellow blossoms draw attention. This member of the squash family is the buffalogourd, or coyote melon, whose fruits, about the size and shape of tennis balls, are particularly noticeable in winter when the rest of the plant has been reduced to a few dried stringy stems.

The common sunflower and a close relative, the golden crownbeard, are among the few plants with conspicuous blossoms which brighten spots where there is sufficient moisture for their growth along roadsides and in depressions between stabilized dunes. Insects wallow in their pollen, and seed-eating birds stop to dine on the matured fruit heads. Another noticeable yellow roadside flower, which blooms in May and again following the late summer rains, is the woolly paperflower. After the blossoms mature the petals fade to pale yellow, become papery, and remain on the plant for weeks.

Because of their large size and the fact that they are prominent among the marginal dunes as gypsum mound-builders, both rubber rabbitbrush and skunkbush sumac stimulate interest. Skunkbush is a close relative of the infamous poison ivy and poison oak but is itself quite harmless. The name "skunkbush" stems from the musky odor developed by the leaves as they dry and turn deep red in autumn. The tiny yellow spring flowers grow in clusters that develop into bunches of orange-red berries with a pleasant acid taste, eaten by birds and other small animals.

Rubber rabbitbrush is a coarse grey-green shrub whose small bright yellow blossoms cover each plant in late summer with a blanket of gold. Their fetid odor draws swarms of insects which, in turn, attract fly-catching birds. Sap of the rabbitbrush contains rubber latex of high quality but not in sufficient quantities to make the plant of commercial consequence. In White Sands National Monument, where no grazing is permitted, rubber rabbitbrush retains its normal place in the plant community, but on heav-

Pink flowers of White Sands sandverbena

Claretcup echinocereus, or torch cactus.

ily used ranges sometimes becomes a dominant species. Unpalatable, it is not eaten by cattle; hence, like cactus, it takes over the land vacated by other plants which have been destroyed or weakened by overgrazing.

Although cactuses are not numerous, three species are found among the shrubs on flats bordering the marginal dunes. Most conspicuous is the claretcup echinocereus, or torch cactus, with its bright-red flowers and large cucumberlike spine-covered stems. The shrubby walkingstick cholla provides protected nesting sites for birds, and the Engelmann pricklypear, with its flat padlike stems and large yellow flowers, attracts attention when the plants are in bloom.

50

BIRDS OF THE DUNELAND

*U*nlike strictly earth-bound animals, some species of birds travel long distances. The majority, at each end of their annual migration flights, settle down within a specific territory to which they return each year. Of the 144 species of birds recorded within White Sands National Monument, most are "just passing through" but stay long enough to rest, find food, and sometimes be identified. Some stop on their migratory spring flights to northern nesting grounds, others are autumn travelers heading south to warmer lands where winters are less severe and food is plentiful. Yet there is a substantial bird population which makes the monument its home. At least eight species nest here, and more than a dozen others are resident during a considerable part of the year.

Because of the profusion and variety of plants and the numbers of insects that they attract, the yucca-sumac and the gramagrass-joint-fir associations among and surrounding the marginal dunes provide food and shelter for an appreciable number of bird species, which usually keep well hidden in the vegetation.

Great horned owls hunt at night and so are not often seen by visitors. They nest in larger cottonwoods among marginal dunes, remaining quiet during daylight hours. Winging low over peripheral dunes and brushy lands of the Tularosa Basin east of them, these silent predators of the night help coyotes and foxes control the populations of kangaroo rats, woodrats, harvest mice, and other night-roaming rodents. Horned owls are not averse to a meal of skunk, and their nests often carry a trace of the odor.

Another winged hunter of the evening hours is the lesser, or Texas nighthawk, which feeds on insects it catches in coursing back and forth only a few feet above the ground. It is not a true hawk but is a relative of the whip-poor-will.

Several species of insect-eating birds that are active in daytime frequent the brushlands near and among the marginal dunes. Among these are the gnatcatcher, western wood pewee, western kingbird, and the Traill's, ash-throated and gray flycatchers. Another flycatcher that may usually be found around headquarters and utility buildings of the monument, where it nests inside open sheds or beneath overhanging eaves, is the buffy Say's phoebe.

51

Also frequenting the vicinity of human habitations, the house finch, or linnet, nests in the monument, often choosing a spot among the spines of a cholla for its nest. The cheerful canary-like songs of the red-crowned males provide a welcome early spring greeting at the visitor center. Two other songsters, whose subdued musical performances are rarely heard by monument visitors because the birds find suitable nesting sites in brushy areas bordering the dunes, are crissal thrashers and

Young loggerhead shrike which has just dined on lizard too long for its digestive capacity.

black-throated sparrows.

Mockingbirds, several species of warblers, white-crowned, sage, and Lincoln's sparrows, and mourning doves are among the more abundant birds that visitors may expect to see among roadside shrubs bordering marginal dunes. Occasionally a medium-sized, black-and-white bird with short rapidly vibrating wings is seen flying low in the same areas. This is the loggerhead, or Sonora, shrike, feared by sparrows and other small birds which constitute part of its diet. Insects, day-active rodents, lizards, and small birds make up the menu of this so-called "butcher bird." The State bird of New Mexico, the roadrunner, although not common, is apparently a year-round resident of the monument.

Conspicuous because of their contrasting color, ravens are sometimes seen walking awkwardly about on the sands or flying low over the dunes. Black-throated sparrows, horned larks, water pipits, sage sparrows, and an occasional loggerhead shrike are sometimes seen among grass clumps of the interdunal flats. The vegetated, parabolic dune region carries a wide variety of nesting birds during summer: orioles, several species of flycatchers, thrashers, flickers, and others.

BIRDS OF GARTON POND

*A*n extension of White Sands National Monument, directly east of headquarters, contains a large marsh with several acres of open water. The marsh is not natural, its development beginning in 1916 when a well drilled for oil struck an artesian flow of warm highly mineralized gypsum water. The pond is shallow, not more than four feet deep, and contains considerable widgeongrass and nitella, or muskgrass. The shores and shallower places support a dense growth of narrow-leaf cattail, saltgrass, and some bulrush. A few naturalized tamarisk, or saltcedar, grow along the southern shore of the open-water part of the marsh.

Since this marsh is located in a semidesert region, it forms a highly attractive stopping place for birds, especially waterfowl, which follow the Tularosa Basin in their seasonal migrations. By far the greatest number of individuals is seen during the spring and fall. Approximately four-fifths of the species that have been recorded in the monument were observed in and

Garton Pond is bordered by growths of saltcedar and bulrushes.

about this marsh, which has been variously called Garton Pond, Garton Lake, Garton Well, and the Pool of Siloam. Most of the species recorded are migratory; the American coot, Virginia rail, and red-winged blackbird are the only ones found nesting in the marsh. Other species, including falcons and hawks (13 species), the short-eared owl, swallows, wrens, robins, warblers, yellow-headed blackbirds, dickcissels, towhees, sparrows, and many others, frequent the marsh for long or short periods of time. About one-fifth of the species spend part of the winter here. Some, such as the marsh hawk, short-eared owl, and pintail and shoveler ducks have been recorded at the marsh during every month of the year although they are not positively known to nest in the monument.

As might be expected, the marsh and pond attract large numbers of migrating waterfowl, including wading and shorebirds. Most of these frequent the area during February, March, and April. They include great blue herons, belted kingfishers, eared grebes, an occasional white pelican, snowy egrets, white-faced ibises, common snipes, sandpipers, willets, black-necked stilts, Wilson's phalaropes, ring-billed gulls, black terns, snowy plovers, killdeers, and long-billed curlews. Both killdeers and curlews are believed to nest in the monument because very young birds have been seen and adults remain throughout the spring and summer.

Visitors to Garton Pond may usually find small flocks of migrating ducks on the open water during the spring and fall. Species most likely to be seen are mallard, American widgeon, pintail, teal, shoveler, redhead, lesser scaup, and an occasional canvasback. Snow geese are infrequent visitors.

Sparrow hawks are often seen in the vicinity of Garton Pond.

Photo courtesy of Bill Bromberg.

MAN AT WHITE SANDS AND VICINITY

Indians

*B*etween 10,000 and 15,000 years ago, scattered bands of nomadic Indians hunted over much of North America. Scientists refer to one of the earliest cultures as Folsom. The people used a projectile with a distinctively shaped stone tip, and several Folsom points have been found in the vicinity of White Sands.

About six centuries ago, farming people occupied small villages along the slopes of the Sacramento Mountains and in the Tularosa Basin. They cultivated corn, beans, pumpkins, and

55

possibly cotton. The architecture of their buildings, ruins of which have been found and studied by archeologists, indicate cultural influences from three directions: from the Salinas area to the north, the Mimbres Valley to the west, and Chihuahua to the south. Although we find no evidence that these people wandered out among the dunes, they doubtless knew them and searched them for anything of interest or use.

Campsites of Indian hunters who lived in this region during more recent times have been found along the east and south margins of the duneland. Some of these sites were probably used by Mescalero Apaches, known to have come to the area

Stone axes give extra sign of early Indian presence.

Campsites of Indian hunters have been found along the south and east margins of the duneland.

for salt. Their campfires heated the gypsum to form plaster of paris, and subsequent rains caused the plaster to set. The hard crust formed has resisted erosion, and the old hearths are now elevated above the level of the adjacent ground. Stone implements and charcoal are additional evidences of early-day Indian activities found here. The Mescaleros ranged from the Rio Grande to the Staked Plains of Texas and were allied with both the Mimbres Apaches of western New Mexico and the Lipan Apaches of the southern Plains. At present most members of the tribe live on a reservation in the mountains northeast of the White Sands.

Spaniards

The remains of a primitive wooden two-wheeled ox cart, which apparently remained buried for many years beneath the

Sand-blasted remains of ancient Spanish carreta found among the dunes and now on display at the Monument headquarters. The small model above approximated original appearance of the ox cart. White-painted portions represent parts of original.

sand, was discovered after a dune moved on. exposing the carreta to view. This relic, now on display in the White Sands National Monument museum, encourages belief that Spaniards of the 17th and 18th centuries knew of the white sands. However, the infamous Jornado del Muerto (Journey of Death), which was a part of the Spanish trade route, the Camino Real, between Mexico City and Santa Fe via El Paso del Norte, followed the Rio Grande valley on the west side of the Franklin, Organ, San Andres, and Oscura Mountains. Apparently Spaniards avoided the white sands and had little interest in the entire Tularosa Basin.

Cattle Ranchers

Historian C. L. Sonnichsen refers to the Tularosa Basin as "The laboratory for the science of doing without." Without shade, without potable water, without much grass, and without wild game, it held little attraction for settlers during the pioneering period of the Southwest. Except for a small sawmill (La Maquina) built before 1800 and protected from Apache attack by a guard of Mexican soldiers, there were no settlements in the basin until November 1862, when a group of Spanish Americans founded the town of Tularosa.

Starting with the end of the Civil War, there began a great westward migration of Texas cattlemen that overflowed into the valleys of central New Mexico by 1886. The Tularosa Basin, including the white duneland, became a vast cattle range, with the inevitable squabbles over range and water rights and shootings as the result of cattle rustling and personal feuds.

Oliver Lee, one of the ranchers, was selected by owners of the small cow outfits to serve as their leader in opposing the big cattle barons who, they felt, were trying to crowd them out. He became involved in several gun fights and fortified his ranch near the mouth of Dog Canyon in the Sacramento Mountains. Years later, when the National Park Service purchased the property to obtain Dog Canyon water rights, some thought was given to converting the Lee ranchhouse into a historical pioneer museum.

Dog Canyon claims historical significance because it contained the "Eyebrow Trail," a steep and treacherous part of an old Indian travel route. On several occasions during the period

58

of Mexican occupation, soldiers followed Apaches into Dog Canyon, engaging them in running fights. After the United States took over the country in 1848, the cavalry fought at least three engagements with Apaches in Dog Canyon.

Conflict between small cattlemen and large cow outfits came to a head with murder of a Las Cruces lawyer, Col. Albert Jennings Fountain, and his eight-year-old son near "point of the sands" at the southern end of the dune area on February 1, 1896. Oliver Lee and one of his companions were placed on trial for the murder but were cleared. Lee continued living in the community as a highly respected citizen, and was twice elected to the New Mexico Legislature.

Perhaps the most famous personality claimed by the Tularosa Basin was Eugene Manlove Rhodes, whose stories of cowboys and cattlemen appeared in various magazines. During the period from 1905 until his death in 1934, Rhodes published 14 novels and novelettes and 60 short stories, all with a southern New Mexico setting. More than a fiction writer, Rhodes was a defender of cowmen and an interpreter of their way of life. C. L. Sonnichsen calls him "the only authentic bard that the cow country has produced." Rhodes Pass in the San Andres Mountains west of the north end of the white sands was named in his memory.

THE WHITE SANDS: COMMERCIAL CONSIDERATIONS

*L*ong considered by local people as a worthless if curious desert, the great expanse of almost pure gypsum caught the attention of promoters who realized that here, without the need for mining, was enough raw material for plaster and wallboard manufacturers the world over for many years. Gypsum, however, is such a common mineral and so abundant and widespread that the isolated location of the Tularosa Basin deposit made its commercial exploitation impractical except for local use. Several buildings in Alamogordo are constructed of gypsum blocks. Many buildings in the boom town of Orogrande had walls of plaster from the White Sands.

Few people in the Tularosa Basin thought of the white duneland as a feature of interest to "outsiders." One man, however, knowing that children of all ages like to play in sand, saw in the thousands of acres of clean rippled dunes an immense "sandpile" for enjoyment of young and old. All it needed, he felt, was suitable publicity and good roads.

Tom Charles sold his "dream" to the Chamber of Commerce of Alamogordo and through it to the people of the Tularosa Basin. At about the same time, scientists became interested in the white sands. Here, they discovered, was geology in action, the intricate processes of nature that produced and refined the gypsum continuing unabated just as they had been doing for many centuries. Here was a unique bit of America, where plants and animals had modified their ways of life to conform with the harsh requirements of a strange environment.

Oliver Lee (left) and Tom Charles, both notable figures in history of the Tularosa Basin and White Sands National Monument.

THE WHITE SANDS: A SOURCE OF RECREATION
AND INSPIRATION FOR YOU

*A*s a result of the findings of scientists and the requests of Tularosa Basin people, President Herbert Hoover on January 18, 1933, signed a proclamation creating White Sands National Monument, for the protection and preservation of the unique duneland and its unusual plant and animal communities, and for the enjoyment of this and future generations. The monument was later enlarged to 146,535 acres.

Since then, many hundreds of thousands of Americans and visitors from foreign lands have enjoyed the stimulating experience of driving among gypsum "snowbanks" in midsummer. They have taken off their shoes and stockings to play in the soft clean white gypsum; and they have felt the thrill of discovery, after climbing to the top of a high dune, at the inspiring view over the vast sea of undulating, yet motionless, whitecaps. Hundreds of photographers, both amateur and professional, have gloried in the intricate ripple patterns covering the dunes and have gasped in disbelief at the high light readings registered by their exposure meters.

During and since World War II, visitors among the dunes have watched airplanes from nearby Holloman Air Force Base circling overhead. They have asked the location of Trinity, where the first nuclear test bomb was detonated, in July 1945, ushering in the atomic age. They have marveled at thin white smoke trails far to the south, where experimental rockets traced vapor paths across the deep blue New Mexico sky. On some occasions the monument has been closed and visitors asked to stay away from the dunes "just in case" one of the big missiles should stray off course and crash into the sands. Several have, for 30 to 40 miles south of the monument are located rocket launching pads of the White Sands Missile Range, where many of America's military and space missiles have been tested in their experimental stages. With the space age at hand, the vast white land of sand is surrounded by intricate tracking and measuring devices that will have an important part in guiding the future history of our world. The boundaries of White Sands National Monument may be said to adjoin the frontiers of space.

The Monument visitor center building houses a museum telling the fascinating story of the White Sands.

Picnicking is popular, and the National Park Service provides tables, fireplaces, and shelters on a large flat in the heart of the duneland of White Sands.

ADDITIONAL READING

For persons who desire to obtain more details of the fascinating story of the gypsum dunes and the interrelationships
of the plants and animals that form the life communities inhabiting them and of the interesting human history of the Tularosa Basin, the following references are suggested. Several,
especially the scientific papers, furnished the material for this
publication.

AMOS, WILLIAM H. *The Life of a Sand Dune.* Scientific American, v. 201,
no. 1, pp. 91-99. 1959.

BAGNOLD, R. A. *The Physics of Blown Sand and Desert Dunes.* Methuen
and Co., Ltd., London. 1954.

BELKNAP, WILLIAM JR. *New Mexico's Great White Sands.* National Geographic Magazine, v. CXII, no. 1, 1957.

BENSON, SETH B. *Concealing Coloration Among Some Desert Rodents of
the Southwestern United States.* Univ. Calif. Pubs. in Zoology, no. 40.
1933.

BLAIR, W. FRANK. *Ecological Distribution of Mammals in the Tularosa
Basin, New Mexico.* Univ. Mich. Contr. from the Lab. of Vertebrate
Zoology, no. 20. 1934.
        *Annotated List of Mammals of the Tularosa Basin,
New Mexico.* American Midland Naturalist, v. 26, no. 1, pp. 218-229.

BUGBEE, ROBERT E. *Notes on Animal Occurrence and Activity in the White
Sands National Monument, New Mexico.* Kansas Academy of Science,
Trans. v. 15, pp. 315-321. 1942.

CHARLES, MRS. TOM. *Tales of the Tularosa.* Guynes Printing Co., El Paso,
Texas. 1959.

CHARLES, MRS. TOM. *More Tales of the Tularosa.* Bennett Printing Co.,
Alamogordo, N. Mex. 1961.

DICE, LEE R., and BLOSSOM, PHILIP M. *Studies of Mammalian Ecology in
Southwestern North America, with Special Attention to the Colors of
Desert Animals.* Carnegie Institution of Washington, Pub. no. 485.
1937.

DIXON, JAMES R. and MEDICA, PHILIP A. *Summer Food of Four Species of
Lizards from the Vicinity of White Sands, New Mexico.* Los Angeles
County Museum Contributions in Science No. 121. 1966.

EMERSON, FRED W. *An Ecological Reconnaissance in the White Sands,
New Mexico.* Ecology, v. XVI, no. 2. 1935.

HOOPER, EMMET T. *Mammals of the Lava Fields and Adjoining Areas in
Valencia County, New Mexico.* Univ. Mich. Misc. Zoological Pubs.
no. 51. 1941.

KELEHER, WILLIAM A. *The Fabulous Frontier.* Santa Fe, N. Mex. 1945.

KOTTLOWSKI, F. E. *Lake Otero - Second Phase in Formation of New
Mexico's Gypsum Dunes.* Geol. Soc. of Ar. Bull., Vol. 69, pp 1733-
1734. 1958.

KUENEN, P. H. *Sand.* Scientific American v. 202, no. 4, pp. 94-110. 1960.

Lowe, Charles H., Jr., and Norris, Kenneth S. *A Sub-species of the Lizard Sceloporus undulatus from the White Sands of New Mexico.* Herpetologica. Vol. 12, pp. 125-127. 1956.

McKee, E. D. *Structures of Dunes at White Sands National Monument, New Mexico.* Vol. 7, no. 1. pp. 69. 1966.

Pray, Lloyd C. *Geology of the Sacramento Mountains Escarpment, Otero County, New Mexico.* Bulletin 35, New Mexico Institute of Mining and Technology, Socorro, N. Mex. pp. 144. 1961.

Russell, Carl P. *The White Sands of Alamogordo.* National Geographic Magazine, v. LXVIII, no. 2. 1935.

Schaffner, Edward Ray. *Flora of the White Sands National Monument, New Mexico.* Thesis submitted to the Graduate Committee for the Degree of Master of Science in Biology, New Mexico A. and M. College. (Copy of ms. is also available at White Sands National Monument.) 1948.

Shields, Lora M. *Gross Modifications in Certain Plant Species Tolerant of Calcium Sulfate Dunes.* American Midland Naturalist, v. 50, no. 1, pp. 224-237. 1953.
  Zonation of Vegetation within the Tularosa Basin. New Mexico. The Southwest Naturalist, v. 1, no. 2, pp. 49-68. 1956.

Shields, Lora M., and Mangum, William K. *Leaf Nitrogen in Relation to Structure of Leaves of Plants Growing in Gypsum Sand.* Phytomorphology v. 4, nos. 1 and 2, pp. 27-38. 1954.

Sonnichson, C. L. *Tularosa, Last Of The Frontier West.* Devin Adair Co., New York. 1960.

Stroud, C. P. *A Survey of the Insects of White Sands National Monument, Tularosa Basin.* American Midland Naturalist, v. 44, no. 3, pp. 659-677. 1950.

APPENDIX — COMMON AND SCIENTIFIC NAMES OF PLANTS AND ANIMALS

This list of common names and their scientific (Latin) equivalents includes only those plants and animals that are mentioned in the text. Authorities for scientific names of all plants, and for common names of all plants except trees, are the second edition, with supplement 1960, of *Arizona Flora* by Thomas H. Kearney and Robert H. Peebles, and *Texas Plants —A Checklist and Ecological Summary*, by F. W. Gould, Texas Agricultural Experiment Station, College Station, Texas, 1962. Authority for common names of trees is *Check List of Native and Naturalized Trees of the United States (Including Alaska)*, by Elbert L. Little, Jr. (U. S. Department of Agriculture Handbook No. 41, published in 1953). Valuable later material on trees, based on above, is in *Southwestern Trees*, by Elbert L. Little, Jr. (U. S. Department of Agriculture Handbook No. 9 - 104 pages).

Scientific and common names of birds are based on the American Ornithologists' Union *Check-List of North American Birds*, Fifth Edition (1957); and for amphibians and reptiles, on *Common Names for North American Amphibians and Reptiles*, Copeia, 1956, No. 3, pp. 172-185. Authority for scientific names of mammals is *List of Recent North American Mammals*, published in 1955 as Bulletin 205 of the U. S. National Museum, whereas the common names of mammals are based on the second edition (1964) of *A Field Guide to the Mammals*, by William H. Burt and Richard P. Grossenheider, and *The Mammal Guide*, by Ralph S. Palmer, 1954.

When there is conflict in spelling between any of the above listed authorities and the *U. S. Government Printing Office Style Manual*, the latter takes precedence.

PLANTS

Aster, tansyleaf—*Aster tanacetifolius*

Bacteria, purple sulfur—*Lamprocystis roseo-percina*

Bluestem, little—*Andropogon scoparius*

Buffalogourd—*Cucurbita foetidissima*

Bulrush, alkali—*Scirpus paludosus*

Cattail, narrowleaf—*Typha angustifolia*

Cholla, walkingstick—*Opuntia imbricata*

Comandra, western—*Comandra pallida*

Cottonwood, Rio Grande—*Populus fremontii*, var. *wislizenii*

Creosotebush—*Larrea tridentata*

Crownbeard, golden—*Verbesina encelioides*

Echinocereus, claretcup—*Echinocereus triglochidiatus*

65

PLANTS (Cont'd)

Ephedra, Torrey—*Ephedra torreyana*

Evening-primrose, Hartweg—*Oenothera hartwegii*

Evening-primrose, yellow flowered —*Oenothera runcinata,* var. *gypsophila*

Frankenia—*Frankenia jamesii*

Gilia—*Gilia pumila*

Grass, chino—*Bouteloua breviseta*

Greggia, mesa—*Nerisyrenia camporum*

Groundsel, broom—*Senecio spartioides*

Jimmy-weed — *Aplopappus heterophyllus*

Loco, halfmoon—*Astragalus allochrous*

Mentzelia, yellow—*Mentzelia pumila*

Mesquite, common—*Prosopis juliflora*

Moonpod, gyp—*Selinocarpus lancedatus*

Nitella—*Nitella sp.*

Pepperweed, mountain — *Lepidium montanum,* var. *alyssoides*

Pickleweed—*Allenrolfea occidentalis*

Pricklypear, Engelmann — *Opuntia engelmannii*

Psilostrophe, woolly — *Psilostrophe tagetina*

Rabbitbrush, rubber — *Chrysothamnus nauseosus,* var. *latisquameus*

Rabbitbrush, southwest — *Chrysothamnus pulchellus*

Ricegrass, Indian—*Oryzopsis hymenoides*

Rosemarymint, hoary—*Pol'omintha incana*

Sacaton, alkali—*Sporobolus airoides*

Saltbush, fourwing—*Atriplex canescens*

Saltcedar—*Tamarix gallica*

Saltgrass—*Distichlis stricta*

Sandverbena, narrowleaf—*Abronia angustifolia*

Seda, scurfy—*Seda lepidota*

Snakeweed, broom—*Gutierrezia sarothrae*

Spectaclepod—*Dithyraea wislizenii*

Sumac, skunkbush—*Rhus trilobata*

Sunflower, common—*Helianthus annuus*

Widgeongrass—*Ruppia maritima*

Yucca, soaptree—*Yucca elata*

MAMMALS

Badger—*Taxidae taxus berlandieri*

Cottontail, desert—*Sylvilagus audubonii minor*

Coyote—*Canis latrans texensis*

Fox, gray—*Urocyon cinereoargenteus scottii*

Fox, kit—*Vulpes macrotis neomexicana*

Gopher, chestnut-faced pocket— *Cratogeomys castanops castanops*

Gopher, eastern (sands) pocket— *Geomys arenarius brevirostris*

Gopher, Mexican pocket—*Cratogeomys castanops lacrimalis*

Jackrabbit, blacktail—*Lepus californicus texianus*

Mouse, Apache pocket—*Perognathus apache gypsii*

Mouse, desert pocket—*Perognathus penicillatus eremicus*

Mouse, long-tailed, deer—*Peromyscus maniculatus blandus*

Mouse, northern grasshopper—*Onychomys leocogaster ruidosae*

Mouse, silky pocket—*Perognathus flavus flavus*

Mouse, southern grasshopper—*Onychomys torridus torridus*

Mouse, western harvest—*Reithrodontomys megalotis megalotis*

Porcupine — *Erethizon dorsatum couseii*

Rat, bannertail kangaroo—*Dipodomys spectabilis baileyi*

Rat, Merriam's kangaroo—*Dipodomys merriamii merriamii*

Rat, Ord's kangaroo—*Dipodomys ordii ordii*

Skunk, striped—*Mephitis mephitis varians*

Squirrel, spotted ground—*Citellus spilosoma canescens*

Woodrat—*Neotoma micropus leucophoea*

BIRDS

Blackbird, red - winged — *Agelaius phoeniceus fortis*

Blackbird, yellow-headed—*Xanthocephalus xanthocephalus*

Canvasback—*Aythya valisineria*

Coot, American—*Fulica americana*

Curlew, long-billed—*Numenius americanus*

66

BIRDS (Cont'd)

Dickcissel—*Spiza americana*

Dove, mourning—*Zenaidura macroura*

Egret, snowy—*Leucophoyx thula*

Falcon, peregrine—*Falco peregrinus anatum*

Falcon, prairie—*Falco mexicanus*

Finch, house—*Carpodacus mexicanus*

Flycatcher, ash - throated—*Myiarchus cinerascens cinerascens*

Flycatcher, gray — *Empidonax wrightii*

Flycatcher, Traill's — *Empidonax traillii*

Gnatcatcher, blue-gray—*Polioptila caerulea amoenissima*

Goose, snow—*Chen hyperborea*

Grebe, eared—*Podiceps caspicus*

Gull, ring-billed—*Larus delawarensis*

Hawk, black—*Buteogallus anthracinus*

Hawk, Cooper's—*Accipiter cooperi*

Hawk, ferruginous—*Buteo regalis*

Hawk, marsh—*Circus cyaneus hudsonius*

Hawk, pigeon—*Falco columbarius*

Hawk, red-tailed—*Buteo jamaicensis*

Hawk, rough-legged—*Buteo lagopus*

Hawk, sharp - shinned — *Accipiter striatus velox*

Hawk, sparrow—*Falco sparverius*

Hawk, Swainson's—*Buteo swainsoni*

Heron, black-crowned night—*Nycticorax nycticorax*

Heron, great blue—*Ardea herodias*

Ibis, white-faced—*Plegadis chihi*

Killdeer—*Charadrius vociferus*

Kingbird, western—*Tyrannus verticalis*

Kingfisher, belted—*Megaceryle alcyon*

Lark, horned—*Eremophila alpestris leucolaema*

Mallard—*Anas platyrhynchos*

Mockingbird—*Mimus polyglottos*

Nighthawk, lesser—*Chordeiles acutipennis texensis*

Owl, great horned—*Bubo virginianus palescens*

Owl, short-eared — *Asio flammeus flammeus*

Pelican, white—*Pelecanus erythrorhynchos*

Pewee, western wood—*Contopus sordidulus*

Phalarope, Wilson's — *Steganopus tricolor*

Phoebe, Say's—*Sayornis saya*

Pintail—*Anas acuta*

Pipit, water—*Anthus spinoletta rubescens*

Plover, snowy—*Charadrius alexandrinus nivosus*

Rail, Virginia—*Rallus limicola*

Raven, common—*Corvus corax*

Raven, white-necked—*Corvus cryptoleucus*

Redhead—*Aythya americana*

Roadrunner—*Geococcyx californianus*

Robin—*Turdus migratorius*

Sandpiper, least—*Erolia minutilla*

Sandpiper, solitary—*Tringa solitaria*

Sandpiper, spotted—*Actitis macularia*

Sandpiper, western—*Ereunetes mauri*

Scaup, lesser—*Aythya affinis*

Shoveler—*Spatula clypeata*

Shrike, loggerhead—*Lanius ludovicianus sonoriensis*

Snipe, common—*Caapella gallinago*

Sparrow, black-throated—*Amphispiza biliniata deserticola*

Sparrow, Brewer's—*Spizella breweri breweri*

Sparrow, clay-colored—*Spizella pallida*

Sparrow, lark—*Chondestes grammacus strigatus*

Sparrow, Lincoln's—*Melospiza lincolnii lincolnii*

Sparrow, sage —*Amphispiza belli nevadensis*

Sparrow, savannah — *Passerculus sandwichensis nevadensis*

Sparrow, western vesper—*Pooecetes graminius confinis*

Sparrow, white-crowned— *Zonotrichia leucophrys gambelii*

Stilt, black - necked — *Himantopus mexicanus*

Swallow, bank—*Riparia riparia riparia*

Swallow, barn—*Hirundo rustica erythrogaster*

Swallow, cliff—*Petrochelidon pyrrhonota*

Swallow, rough-winged—*Stelgidopteryx ruficollis serripennis*

Swallow, tree—*Iridoprocne bicolor*

Swallow, violet-green—*Tachycineta thalassina*

Teal, blue-winged—*Anas discors*

BIRDS (Cont'd)

Teal, cinnamon—*Anas cyanoptera*

Teal, green-winged—*Anas carolinensis*

Tern, black—*Chlidonias niger surinamensis*

Thrasher, crissal—*Toxostoma dorsale dorsale*

Thrasher, sage—*Oreoscoptes montanus*

Towhee, green-tailed — *Chlorura chlorura*

Warbler, Audubon's — *Dendroica auduboni auduboni*

Warbler, orange-crowned—*Vermivora celata orestera*

Warbler, Wilson's—*Wilsonia pusilla pileolata*

Warbler, yellow—*Dendroica petechia sonorana*

Widgeon, American—*Mareca americana*

Willet—*Catoptrophorus semipalmatus*

Wren, Bewick's—*Thryomanes bewickii*

Wren, cactus — *Campylorhynchus brunneicapillum*

Wren, house—*Troglodytes aedon parkmanii*

Wren, long-billed marsh—*Telmatodytes palustris*

Wren, rock—*Salpinctes obsoletus obsoletus*

REPTILES AND AMPHIBIANS

Coachwhip—*Masticophis flagellum*

Kingsnake, prairie — *Lampropeltis calligaster*

Lizard, bleached earless—*Holbrookia maculata ruthveni*

Lizard, collared—*Crotaphytus collaris*

Lizard, Cowles prarie—*Sceloporus undulatus cowlesi*

Lizard, round-tailed horned—*Phrynosoma modestum*

Lizard, side-blotched—*Uta stansburiana*

Lizard, southern prairie—*Sceloporus undulatus consobrinus*

Lizard, Texas horned—*Phrynosoma cornutum*

Rattlesnake, prairie—*Crotalus viridis viridis*

Rattlesnake, western diamondback —*Crotalus atrox*

Snake, checkered garter—*Thamnophis marcianus*

Snake, gopher—*Pituophis melanoleucus*

Snake, long-nosed—*Rhinocheilus lecontei*

Snake, western hognose—*Heterodon nasicus*

Spadefoot, Couch's — *Scaphiopus couchi*

Spadefoot, plains—*Scaphiopus bombifrons*

Spadefoot, western — *Scaphiopus hammondi*

Toad, Great Plains—*Bufo cognatus*

Turtle, yellow box—*Terrapene ornata luteola*

Whiptail, little striped—*Cnemidophorus inornatus*

Whiptail, marbled—*Cnemidophorus tigris marmoratus*

INSECTS AND ARTHROPODS

Ant, acrobat—*Cremastogaster opaca*, var. *punctulata*

Ant, American black—*Lasius niger neoniger*

Ant, carpenter—*Camponotus acutirostris*

Ant, harvester — *Appaenogaster boulderensis*

Aphis, sunflower—*Aphid helianthi*

Beetle, apple flea—*Haltica foliaceae*

Beetle, convergent ladybird—*Hippodamia convergens*

Beetle, darkling—*Eleodes hispilabris*

Beetle, long-horned—*Tragidion armatum*

Beetle, snout—*Eupagaderes cretaceus*

Beetle, tiger—*Cincindela lepida*

Butterfly, sulphur—*Colias eurytheme*

Centipede—*Scolopendra sp.*

Cicada, Townsend's—*Tibicen townsendi*

Cricket, camel—*Ammobaenetes phrixocnemoides arenicolus*

Fly, flesh—*Sarcophaga robusta*

68

INSECTS AND ARTHROPODS (Cont'd)

Fly, robber—*Erax pilosus*

Grasshopper, pallid-winged—*Trimerotropis pallidipennis*

Moth, yucca—*Tegeticula alba*

Scorpion, northern—*Vejovis boreus*

Solpugid—*Eremobates affinis*

Spider. wolf—*Lycosa* sp.

Wasp, chalcid—*Calotaccus aeneoviridis*

Weevil, snout—*Sycphophorus yuccae*

"Good bye" to *White Sands and their weird, unearthly beauty.*

70

Backward glances at shadow witchery in the dunelands.

The roadrunner, New Mexico's State bird, is a year 'round resident of White Sands.

**This booklet is published in cooperation with the National Park Service
by the**

SOUTHWEST PARKS AND MONUMENTS ASSOCIATION

*a non-profit distributing organization pledged to aid
in preservation and interpretation of Southwestern features
of outstanding national interest.*

The Association lists for sale many excellent publications for adults and children and hundreds of color slides on Southwestern subjects. We recommend the following items for additional information on the Southwest and the National Park System:

YOUR NATIONAL PARK SYSTEM IN THE SOUTHWEST, IN WORDS AND COLOR. Jackson. 500 word articles on each National Park Service area in the huge Southwest Region, with full-color photograph for 54 of the 56 areas listed. Most authoritative treatment possible, by 32-year former career N.P.S. employee, with every text checked for accuracy by Regional Office and each area's superintendent. Also contains "How to Get There" appendix. 64 pages, 56 full-color illustrations, color cover, paper. **$1.95**

100 DESERT WILDFLOWERS IN NATURAL COLOR. Dodge. Descriptions and full-color portraits of 100 of the most interesting desert wildflowers. Photographic hints. 64 pp., full-color cover, paper. **$1.50**

100 ROADSIDE WILDFLOWERS OF SOUTHWEST UPLANDS IN NATURAL COLOR. Dodge. Companion book to author's 100 Desert Wildflowers in Natural Color, but for higher elevation flowers. 64 pages and full-color cover, paper. **$1.50**

FLOWERS OF THE SOUTHWEST DESERTS. Dodge and Janish. More than 140 of the most interesting and common desert plants beautifully drawn in 100 plates, with descriptive text. 112 pp., color cover, paper **$1.00**

FLOWERS OF THE SOUTHWEST MESAS. Patraw and Janish. Companion volume to the Desert flowers booklet, but covering the plants of the plateau country of the Southwest. 112 pp., color cover, paper. **$1.00**

FLOWERS OF THE SOUTHWEST MOUNTAINS. Arnberger and Janish. Descriptions and illustrations of plants and trees of the southern Rocky Mountains and other Southwestern ranges above 7,000 feet elevation. 112 pp., color cover, paper. **$1.00**

POISONOUS DWELLERS OF THE DESERT. Dodge. Invaluable handbook for any person living in the desert. Tells the facts about dangerous insects, snakes, etc., giving treatment for bites and stings and dispels myths about harmless creatures mistakenly believed poisonous. 48 pp. ....**$ .60**

MAMMALS OF THE SOUTHWEST DESERTS (formerly Animals of the Southwest Deserts). Olin and Cannon. Handsome illustrations, full descriptions, and life habits of the 42 most interesting and common mammals of the lower desert country of the Southwest below the 4,500-foot elevation. 112 pp., 60 illustrations, color cover, paper. **$1.00**

MAMMALS OF SOUTHWEST MOUNTAINS AND MESAS. Olin and Bierly. Companion volume to Mammals of Southwest Deserts. Fully illustrated in exquisitely done line and scratchboard drawings, and written in Olin's masterfully lucid style. Gives description, ranges, and life habits of the better known Southwestern mammals of the uplands. Color cover, paper **$2.00**
Cloth **$3.25**

Write For Catalog

SOUTHWEST PARKS AND MONUMENTS ASSOCIATION

Box 1562 — Globe, Arizona 85501